Paperback   ISBN: 978-1-7356506-0-9
Hardback   ISBN: 978-1-7356506-1-6

Attention Schools and Businesses:
Wabash to Worthing books are available at quantity discounts with bulk purchase for educational, business, or sales promotional use.
For more information please send an email to:
sales@sherrickacarpenterstanley.com

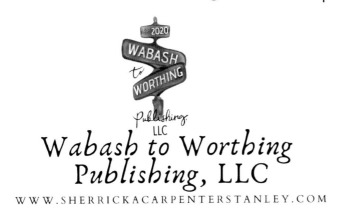

Wabash to Worthing
Publishing, LLC
WWW.SHERRICKACARPENTERSTANLEY.COM

Wabash to Worthing Publishing, LLC
P.O. Box 1974
Greensboro, NC 27402
For Copies and Information:
www.sherrickacarpenterstanley.com
sales@sherrickacarpenterstanley.com

I Fit IN Just Right!

Me & My Family

Story by
Sherricka Carpenter
Stanley

Illustrated by
Audeva Joseph

Dedicated to
Christopher, Cayden & Skylar:
To the ONLY three people who know what my
heartbeat sounds like from the **inside**.
This FIRST one is for YOU!
You **Fit IN Just Right!**

In Mommy's round belly,

Feeding from her is best.

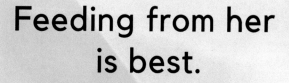

Peekaboo under Daddy,

Asleep on his tired chest.

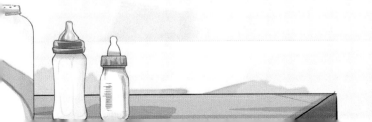

I Fit IN Just Right!

Through my mama's camera lens,

Inside of my daddy's shoes.

"Jimmy legs" laugh
for God Mom,

For God Dad,
only boo-hoos.

I Fit IN Just Right!

Wrapped up on my sister's lap,

On my back,
lil brother
jumps.

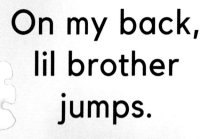

Beside Great-Granny for prayers,

On my head,
Great-Granddad
thumps.

I Fit IN Just Right!

Stuck between my siblings,

In Daddy's
football hold.

Looking from Grandma's chair,

Close to Granddad is gold.

I Fit IN Just Right!

23

Apple of my uncle's eye,

Kissing on Auntie's sweet lips.

Surrounded by MeMaw and cousins,

Sitting close near
PaPaw's hips.

I Fit IN Just Right!

Joking with my uncles,

For my aunties, I dress my best.

Beside my best friend,

Next to
Superman's chest.

I Fit IN Just Right!

31

Up high in winter snow,

Among the springtime trees.

Beneath the summer sand,

Underneath autumn leaves.

Big smiles for a vacation 'pic',

Matching for a holiday one.

Cheering for our
favorite team,

Time with family is fun.

I Fit IN Just Right!

This is my family.

And I Fit IN Just Right!

~Glossary~

Sibling: children having one or both parents in common; brother or sister

Godparents: Guardians who have pledged to help with the upbringing of a child; especially religiously.

"Jimmy Legs": when a child gets wiggly and wants to break free

Preposition –

a word which is placed before a noun or a pronoun to show its relation with something else in the sentence

among	next
beneath	of
beside	on
between	over
by	through
for	to
from	under
in	underneath
inside	up
near	with

Wabash to Worthing
Publishing. LLC

WWW.SHERRICKACARPENTERSTANLEY.COM

AUTHOR

Sherricka Carpenter Stanley is a wife, mother of three (& a bonus daughter) and educator. This life-long learner has decided to use this next chapter in life to fulfill deferred dreams. Look to hear more from Sherricka in different genres of literature.

Born and raised in Durham, NC (Bull City), she now resides with her family in Greensboro, NC. Home of her HBCU alma mater NCA&TSU.

ILLUSTRATOR

Audeva Joseph is a native Haitian, proud daughter and aunt. She is a highly skilled artist. Audeva has helped to bring several childrens books to life through her art.

Made in the USA
Columbia, SC
21 December 2020

29558213R00027